GW00390987

Look at it This Way!

ALLSHARE

SELECTED POETRY AND PROSE
BY JAMES KIRKUP

The Submerged Village
A Correct Compassion
A Spring Journey
The Descent into the Cave
The Prodigal Son
Refusal to Conform
A Bewick Bestiary
Zen Gardens (photo-etchings with Birgit Skiöld)
Paper Windows: Poems from Japan
White Shadows, Black Shadows: Poems of Peace and War
The Body Servant: Poems of Exile
Scenes from Sesshu (photo-etchings with Birgit Skiöld)
To the Ancestral North: Poems for an Autobiography
Cold Mountain Poems
Scenes from Sutcliffe (portfolio of poems and photographs)
The Tao of Water (photo-etchings with Birgit Skiöld)
Insect Summer (children's novel)
The Magic Drum (children's novel)
The Only Child: An Autobiography of Infancy
Sorrows, Passions & Alarms: An Autobiography of Childhood
No More Hiroshimas: Poems & Translations
Selected Poems of Takagi Kyozo
Modern Japanese Poetry
Zen Contemplations
The Guitar Player of Zuiganji
Dengonban Messages: One-Line Poems
Ecce Homo - My Pasolini: Poems & Translations
Fellow Feelings
The Sense of the Visit: New Poems
Throwback: Poems toward an Autobiography
Words for Contemplation: Mantras
Shooting Stars (haiku)
First Fireworks (haiku)
Short Takes (one-line poems)
Blue Bamboo (haiku, senryu, tanka)

Look at it This Way!

Poems for Young People
by
James Kirkup

Drawings by
Sonia Lawson R.A.

Rockingham Press

Published in 1994
by
The Rockingham Press
11 Musley Lane,
Ware, Herts
SG12 7EN

British Library Cataloguing-in-Publication Data

A catalogue record for this book
is available from the British Library

ISBN 1 873468 16 4

Printed in Great Britain
by Biddles Ltd., Guildford

Eastern Arts
Board Funded

CONTENTS

Acknowledgments

Many of these poems have appeared in magazines and anthologies over the last ten years or so, and have been broadcast by the BBC.

THE HOUSE AT NIGHT

Some stealthy spider is weaving round my bed
and mice are nibbling the curtains overhead.
Weird footsteps make the floorboards crack,
the staircase creaks, chill draughts thrill down my back
from some forgotten window out of sight —
    this is the house at night.

There's a whispering on the landing
where a creepy tropic plant is standing,
and the coatrack in the hall
lets fall a scarf — a long, soft fall:
a snake's loose coils that rapidly grow tight —
    this is the house at night.

From the distant kitchen come the notes
of dripping taps, plink-plonking secret codes
I cannot get the meaning of: a sudden
icy shudder — the refrigerator groans — a hidden
oven, cooling, ticks in rustling ember-light —
    this is the house at night.

— But even stranger is my own tense breathing
as I lie here speechless looking at the ceiling
that seems to swim all round like falling snow.
I can hear my eyelids batting gently, slow —
then quick as heartbeats as I freeze with fright
at something in the mirror shining bright —
has someone left the telly on all night?
No, thank heaven, it's all right,
it's only the moon's pale, spooky light
touching my tangled sheets with chalky white —
    yes, this is the house at night.

ASLEEP OR AWAKE

When everyone's asleep at home,
what's going on in the streets outside?
On my dresser the tidy's brush and comb
look into the mirror that tries to hide
(with the curtains drawn on the windowpanes)
the secret life of shunting trains
as they whistle forlornly through the dark,
like the hooting of ships putting out to sea
while the lighthouse beam crashes through the park
and the wind strips the leaves from bush and tree.

And if there's a moon, the shadows it casts
are different from any we know by day:
in the harbour, the sailing ships' rocking masts
stretch and swing with a phantom sway,
throwing mad shapes on the ebbing tide
while the dockyards' iron skeletons ride
like death-ships on the darkling waves,
and crosses are black in the churchyard walls
like vampires hoisting themselves from their graves —
and out of the thatch as a barn-owl calls.

— Is it only in dreams we seem to meet
burglars and murderers running away,
or the tramp of an army's marching feet
off to the wars of another day?
O, out in the streets where nobody goes
the buildings look strange in their moonlit rows,
and their windows look down like big dark eyes
on our house, where curtains and blinds are drawn,
so they cannot see in — where each one lies
asleep (or awake) till the break of dawn.

WHO'S THAT?

Who's that
stopping at
my door in the
dark, deep
in the dead of the moonless night?

Who's
that in the quiet
blackness,
darker than dark?

Who
turns the han-
dle of the door, who
turns the old brass hand-
dle of
my door with never a sound, the handle
that always
creaks and rattles and
squeaks but
now
turns
without a sound, slowly
slowly
    slowly
       round?

Who's that moving through the floor
as if it were a lake, an open door? Who
is it who passes through
what can never be passed through,
who passes through
the rocking chair
without rocking it,

who passes through
the table without knocking it, who
walks out of the cupboard without unlocking it?
Who's that? Who plays with my toys
with no noise, no
noise?

Who's that? Who is it
silent and silver
as things in mirrors, who's
as slow as feathers,
shy as the shivers,
light as a fly?

Who's that who's that
as close as
close as a hug, a kiss —

Who's THIS?

QUESTIONS

Why is the rocking-chair rocking?
　　Why does it rock in the windless air
of the sunny veranda — Why
　　does it rock when there's no one there?

Why is the swing door swinging?
　　Why does it swing at the foot of the stair?
Why, like the chair, does it keep on moving
　　back and forth, when there's no one there?

Why is the doorbell ringing? Why
　　does it ring through the empty flat
when there's nobody pressing the button
　　and nobody stands on the welcome mat?

Something has happened here. What can it be?
　　Why have they all gone away like this?
Why are the windows open? And why
　　does that record keep turning, hiss upon hiss . . . ?

HIGH DIVE

It feels very lonely, up here against the clouds
and girders of the glass roof. The pool so far away,
framed in flowers of a thousand upturned faces.

Walk to the brink, turn, and carefully
(firm toes gripping this last hold on life)
hang heels in space. Face a blank wall.

Raise arms slowly, sideways, shoulder-high,
silent passion, dream-deep concentration
foretelling every second of the coming flight.

Then with a sudden upward beat of palms,
of arms like wings, gathering more than thought
launch backwards into take-off, into one ball

roll for a quadruple reverse somersault
that at the last split second flicks
open like a switchblade —

feet pointed as in prayer, neat-folded hands
stab the heavens like a dagger, plunge
deep into the pool's azure flesh — without a splash.

13

BREAKDANCERS

Our stage is plaza, shopping mall, pedestrian zone,
or the arcade outside the stores on closing day.
Evenings especially, outside Woolworth's or the C & A,
we flock together, man, to rap and break the night away.

The streets are ours as well as yours, and so you stop
and watch in wonder as we strut our breaks. In groups
of five or six we switch our stuff and hip the hop —
we need no classy club to spread our twirls and loops.

And so you see us tumble, shadow-box, do double somersaults
and spin on headstands, handstands, double-jointed tops:
our ghetto-blasters scratch the beat, we pop our joints
to R 'n' B and Rock, with one-hand flips and flops.

They call us breakers, smurfers, scratchers, robot hips.
We do our solo turns — the flopping fish, the head-walk and
the nerveless, boneless pantomime that — though we dance
alone — makes unseen partners take us by the hand.

We are the blacks, hispanics, rejects and the out-of-work.
Our youth is useless in society today. Our energy, for sure,
can not be channelled into army, factory, production line —
and so we break, till bottoms, hands and feet are sore.

But we are young, athletic, acrobatic, tai-chi punks,
we have the look, the caps, the sneakers and the gloves,
the knee-caps, bottom-bumpers, headbands — all the gear
to help us flip and jerk the way the public loves.

They stand and watch us do our turns, and maybe drop
a coin or two into our common pot. We need the dough, to buy
our Adidas or Pumas, Nike Golfs, or ten-feet moquette spreads
we lay on any concourse for a natural high.

We must be fit, and fast, and funny too. We take no drugs, no
smokes.
These rippling spines and fluid limbs are trained and taut and neat
so we break and strut instead of steal and fight —
and speak the universal language of the hip-hop street!

ICE DANCERS

For Torvill and Dean

Under the spotlights, waiting for
the music, that will be a curious mix
of waltz, rock, cha-cha-cha-,
          boogie, paso doble —
there they stand on glittering skates,
in suits of light and rainbow gold,
hands joined, heads high, feet poised
already for the perfect patternings
of speed, strength, poetry and grace.

They seem to hold that proud pose
for an eternity, and with unfailing
smiles of courage for the tests that are to come
of art, invention, skill and charm.
— But now the music starts, and they
at once sweep wide apart, as if
regretfully: yet swerve away in spins
and loops that bring them back together soon.

Their blade heels now etch the ice with curves
that are designs of some divine abstraction,
broken only when they leap as one, and whirl
upon the triple axles of suspended flight,
scattering a ghost of flurried flakes, and then
return to ice, descend so lightly on their shadows,
with eager impulse gliding easily into reverse, then
an arabesque, then crouch, and rise to spin and spin

and spin beneath the spots until they almost
vanish into themselves, a brilliant blur — applause!

— Sometimes one falls, and then it is as if
a legendary bird had half-forgotten how to fly,
but almost immediately remembers, and soars off again
with undeterred self-confidence into the airy realms
of weightlessness, released into the magic space that is
their only element, where only the exceptional can live.

SUNSET KITES

What is this strange delight
in flying a kite?
Why does it tug
at something more
than arms and hands?

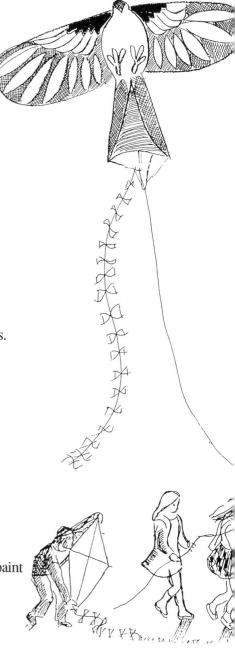

Run against the wind
and feel on your fingers
the lift and pull of the string
as the kite
takes off like an eagle
behind you, above you
into the open sky,
the way of the birds.

This bird is one you hold
not in caring fingers
like a fledgling fallen
into the nest of your cupped hands.

Nor do you carry it proudly
on your wrist, your gauntlet,
like a hawk hooded or unhooded.

Though it is not a living thing,
it has life, a life of its own,
and though you cage it
in cupboard or classroom
it cannot be caged,
and cannot be tamed.

This bird of wood and paper and paint
is your own
personal messenger,
a friend with wings
who flies always

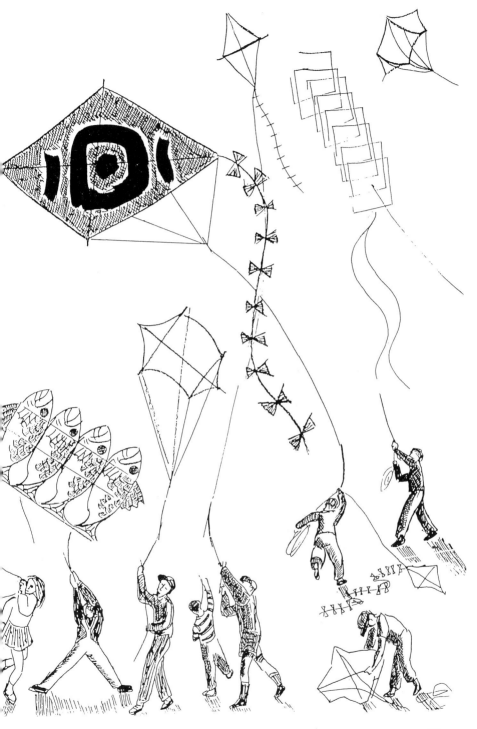

for you alone — in another's hands
it does not respond
as it does to yours'.

And so you run and run
against the wind of light,
the wind that is the water of
this flying fish,
the wind that is the air
of this swimming bird,
the wind that is its only
element — the way of wings,
wings of birds and dragons,
wings of flying kites
like magic carpets.

What is the message of
the sunset kites
that on the evening breeze
above beach or cliff or field
or city playing grounds
twinkle in the gathering dusk
like first stars
or distant snowy peaks
still shining
above darkened earth?

O, let them soar
and sparkle on unending strings
in clouds of glory
and in estuaries of the moon
beyond sandbanks of cloud,
beyond the midnight hour
striking on empty streets —

shimmer through sleep and dreams
like eternal planets
on long ropes of light,
on cords of time,

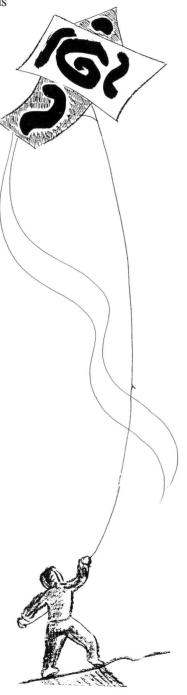

pulling at our happy hands,
tugging at our very hearts,
calling us back into outer space,
into the infinite nothing
from which we came
with kites trailing . . .

— What is this strange delight
in flying a kite?
Why does it tug
at something more
than arms and hands?

PARACHUTE JUMP

Down out of the blue
drops the starfish man,
he who both floats and
sinks into the seas of light,
death-rider, spinning
pinned against the fall
of space, wall of death

As I drift and drop
down, my heaven darkens —
darker, dark as rising
earth, my only sun
that far white target,
cold planet of chalk
deep in a field's green well.
Peaks, bays, forests
whirl like clouds around
my head. A distant lake
explodes its bomb
flash — hurtling air
my body's thunder.
— Will I make it?

Free fall, free
of all but breath
that drinks the wind
giddy with flight —
the ground the ground
coasts nearer, near, sheer
cliff of commonsense.

Starfish man, still
plunging in sands
of space and time — then
thudding ripcord springs
a bud that bursts — O,
many-petalled peony,
white and crimson, sunny,

leisurely unfolding,
lazily unfurling — the relief,
release of winter-crumpled
filaments, fronds, floating
fans of silk whose shadow
dandelions softly down,
collapses sighing on

its own falling petals,
my target poem. — And now,
a creature from outer space
finally stands upright,
looks around him, inhuman,
feet on alien earth, and
hauling in his broken dream.

HANG GLIDER

From some
cliff, bluff
or immaterial
mountain top
shove off —

Surfing the void
jump into flight —
cloud-swimmer
carving a place
in air and light.

Tobogganing
the runs of fall —
a bellyflop
on nothingness
a silent crawl

in seas of space
your flung trapeze
the frail horizon —
handstand on
a swinging breeze.

— Float in the shade
of your rainbow span:
time's easy rider,
plunge into depths
where day began

while earth — below
above — spins like a top
or lifts a sliding
wave of green and brown
where you must drop

to surface, drowned
alive by gravity of ground.

THE HUNTING TRAINS

Down the dark nights of countries, continents,
the great trains on their glittering tracks
go hunting like wild beasts in the jungles of sleep,
across plains, mountains, valleys, shires,
hooting, growling, whistling and screaming as
they thunder and plunge through trees and tunnels
with eyes blazing, nostrils flaring, hair streaming fire,
on pinions of flame and pistons of smoke and steam
with wheels of iron and claws of steel
they shriek through the cities, villages and towns,
pouncing on helpless hamlets and halts,
pillaging, looting and smashing, and slyly
creeping along embankments, ready to strike
at the next crossing, the next
unguarded signal-box —
making bridges and aqueducts
and the sheer brick clouds of viaducts
shake to their roots as they hear the approaching
menacing tread of the hunting trains, hunting
even the river, the lake and the ocean bed,
hunting and haunting with faraway grumbles and moans
the sleep and dreams of all who are sleeping and dreaming
with visions of fiery steeds, burning tigers, brazen eagles —
and striking terror to the heart of the sleepless woods.

ODE TO A DE LUXE EXPRESS TRAIN

(From the French of Valery Larbaud)

Give me your grand sounds, your movement so smooth,
your nocturnal gliding all across illuminated Europe,
O superb de luxe express! and O the disturbing musics
That go surging along your corridors of rich gilded leather,
Behind whose lacquered doors, with their locks of ponderous brass,
All the millionaires lie sleeping.

I run softly singing along your swaying corridors,
Following your voice to Vienna, Budapest,
Mingling my one voice with your hundred thousand voices,
O you great harmonica-train!
I first realized how lovely life might be
In a compartment of the Nord-Express, between Wirballen and Pskow.
We were gliding across plains where shepherds,
Standing under clumps of huge trees round as hills,
Were clad in coarse, dirty sheepskins...
Eight o'clock on an autumn morning, and the beautiful prima donna
With the violet eyes was vocalizing in the next compartment.

And you, grand plate glass windows through which
I watched Siberia pass by, and the Mountains of Samnium,
Castille harsh and blossomless, and the Sea of Marmara under steaming rain!

Give me, O, Orient Express, Sud-Brenner-Bahn, O give me
Your miraculous heavy poundings, and
Your vibrant voice, like thrushes trilling:
Give me that light, easy breathing
Of tall, slender long-distance locomotives
Hauling effortlessly four yellow carriages with golden lettering
In the mountainous solitudes of Serbia
And, further on, crossing Bulgaria all roses ...

Ah! let those sounds and those movements
Enter my poetry and speak for me,
Describe my indescribable life, my life
Of a child with no wish to know anything but
An endless longing for undiscovered places.

(From *Les Poésies d'A.O. Barnabooth : Paris, Gallimard*)

THE HAUNTED LIFT

On the ground floor
of this ultramodern
tower block

in the dead
middle
of the night

the lift doors
open, with a
clang.

Nobody enters,
and nobody
comes out.

In the dead
middle
of the night

the lift doors
close with a clang,
and the lift begins

to move
slowly
up —

with nobody in it,
nobody but
the ghost of a girl

who lived here once
on the thirteenth floor of
this ultramodern tower block

*

One day, she went to play
in an old part of town,
and never came back.

She said she was just
going to the corner shop,
but she never came home.

Now her ghost
keeps pressing
in the dead

middle of the night
the button
for the thirteenth floor.

But when the door
opens with a clang
she cannot step out.

She gazes longingly
at the familiar landing,
but only for a moment —

then the lift doors
clang in her face
and her tears

silently flow
as the lift
in the dead

middle
of the night

so soft and slow

carries her down again
down below,
far, far below

the ground
floor, where nobody
waits for the haunted lift

in the dead
middle
of the night.

*

Sometimes
on the thirteenth floor
her mother and father

with her photo
beside their bed
wake up

in the dead
middle of the night, and hear
the mysterious clanging

of closing lift doors,
and wonder
who it could be

in the dead
middle
of the night

using the lift
at such
an unearthly hour.

— In this ultramodern
tower block
there is no thirteenth floor.

HAPPY HAIKU

Swimming in the rain
in summer pools — trudging through
deep snow at Christmas.

Holding fresh-baked bread
in my cold hands, then taking
the first bite — with jam.

The rainy playground —
riding my bicycle with
an umbrella up.

Walking on tall stilts
round the garden, and tumbling
on the rubbish-heap.

Playing in the band,
blowing my trumpet, trying
to drown the bass drum.

Knitting a muffler —
blue, purple, green, orange stripes —
knitting a muffler.

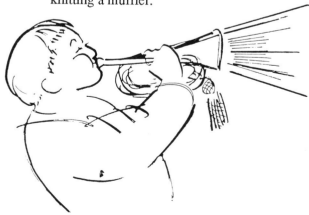

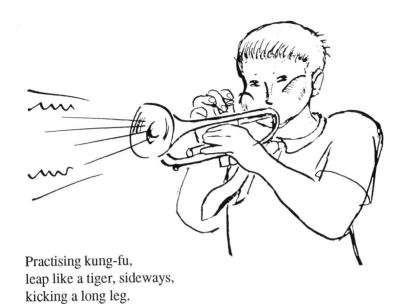

Practising kung-fu,
leap like a tiger, sideways,
kicking a long leg.

Reading by the fire,
turning the pages quickly
to the very end.

TANKA *

Kyoto Winter

Like the seven stars
grouped in the constellation
of Ursa Major, hanging
on their one bare bough —
dusky-red, last persimmons.

Reflection

Outside the window
a strange face is looking in
with a funny smile.
— I wonder who it could be?
Oh, good grief, it's only me!

Bright Kitchen

Turn the door handle,
switch off the light behind you,
walk down the passage
in darkness. Turn another
handle, to the bright kitchen.

* *"tanka"* is a classical Japanese poetic form of five lines, in
which there are respectively 5,7,5,7, and 7 syllables in all.

POLAR BEAR

Hugging the wall, down
there in his open pit,
he ambles absently,
fitting his whole body
to the wide curve
of dingy cement.

Backwards and forwards
loping, big head weaving,
pressing one matted flank
and then the other
to the sun-scorched cliff
of his lonely prison.

His coat is far from white — rather
a drab cream, with
yellow or brownish stains.
— He looks unhappy in the heat.
No wonder he never

turns to growl at
us, begging for attention.

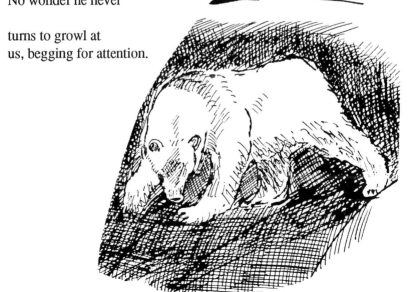

THE KITTEN IN THE FALLING SNOW

This year- old kitten
has never seen snow,
fallen or falling, until now
this late winter afternoon.

He sits with wide eyes
at the first firelit window, sees
white things falling
from black trees.

Are they petals, leaves or birds?
They cannot be the cabbage whites
he batted briefly with his paws,
or the puffball seeds in summer grass.

They make no sound, they have no wings
and yet they can whirl and fly around
until they swoop like swallows, and
disappear into the ground.

"Where do they go?" he questions
with eyes ablaze, mewing faintly, following
their flight into black stone. So I put him
out in the yard, to make their acquaintance.

He has to look up at them: when one
blanches his coral nose, he sneezes,
and flicks a few from his whiskers, from
his sharpened ear, that picks up silences.

He catches one on a curled-up paw
and licks it quickly, purring, before
its strange milk fades, then sniffs its ghost,
a wetness, while his sable coat

shivers with stars of sparkling frost.
— And with something else that makes his thin
tail swish, his fur stand on end! Then
he suddenly scoots into the house again

and sits again with wide eyes, mewing
faintly at the firelit window, seeing
white things falling, falling
from black trees.

MISFIT

(for a dead kitten)

In the new litter, you were the one
we cared least for. You never knew why.
Black like your mother, and like her
marked with a white star on your chest.
But — so unlike her (half-wild
in her dignified self-absorption) —
greedy and pushing and clumsy.

From the start we rejected you,
had to drive you away from the dish
to give the rest a chance, and gradually
you began to understand you were not liked.
The others rejected you too, even your mother.
Your look of mute incomprehension
was intelligent, but blank — not just pathetic.

*

That look still masks your face with silence
as you lie now in the gutter,
run over by the rear offside wheel
under which you had been sheltering
from the rain, and our unkindness.
— You foolish, frantic little beast,
why didn't you, as you had always done,

run when you heard the engine warming? No. You
stayed true to your awkward nature, had to wait
until your back was broken before you tried
to alter the pattern of your fate,
and scrambled dying in final indignity,
but silent still, from the horror of our gaze
that you alone had shifted out of neutral.

NO PLACE LIKE HOME

The hermit crab
prefers to dwell
in somebody else's
vacant shell.

But as he grows
it gets too tight, so
he has to find another
strong but light.

It must not be
too heavy, for
he has to carry it
along the shore.

So he scuttles
from dawn to dusk
looking for a more
accommodating husk.

From cockles and winkles
to the largest shells —
these are the hermitages
where he dwells.

When he has found one
he wriggles right inside —
yet the house on his back
is no place to hide.

There's nowhere he can be at home,
he's always on the run,
until he finds himself at last
right back where he'd begun —

Without a roof,
without a friend:
this is the way
all hermits end.

THE HOUSE UNDER THE SEA

Bright chains of bubbles, ropes of shining smoke,
twist from the chimneys in the current's shiftless breeze
as these last tenants of the airless property, the drifting house
depart, hearing the sea's loud keys piercing the draughty lock.

No, it is not rain that makes the slates shine bleak
in thundering showers under the deep's green mountains.
No — someone left the garden gate unlatched, and fountains
flooded down from the massive sky, turning the sunlight dark.

Who is this, mounting the stair with sure and stumbling tread?
What heavy ghost is this, that blunders at all the doors?
Listen! Monsters lie imprisoned under the bedroom floors,
and into the melting ceiling floats a double unmade bed.

Mirror, you who in the green-spotted darkness of your caves
seemed to contain an image cast away on a deserted tide,
now fill with real sea again; and bitter brine, instead
of that vanished face's warm and cryptic tears, blackens your leaves

of silvery memory, draws from the walls your tarnished nails,
and to the undulating carpet lets you soundlessly and slowly spin.
— What uninvited guest is this? Who can have let him in,
this clumsy visitor who scatters the rooms with weeds and shells?

*

Somewhere, an endless cradle rocks. As birds, once, in light and air
above the roar of wind, the intermittent ticking of dismembered clocks
litters the sullen stillness now, lulls in the crashing of the rocks
on whale-lighted windows, and the shriek of curtains that the stir

of the gentle ocean-minotaur destroys, or the stroking hands
of giant octopuses wrench amiably, gracefully devour as they drag them lov
— All fire is out, but from the black hearth pour like a slow
dream of smoke wide wreaths of falling soot, staining the amber sands.

O, is this a man's, this open mouth that once declared its wish
with vigour — these limbs that could kill, hands that once
                                        could caress and wound?
Can this wreck be life's wonder, who drinks now the wine of the drowned?
— At a dissolving pane looks in, and enters, curiously,
                                        the first, pale, pointed,
                                        staring fish ...

THE CHILDREN OF CHANGE

"The Universe is transformation: our life is what our thoughts make it."
                                        (Marcus Aurelius: Meditations)

We are the children of change.
Whatever we think of, we can become —
a horse, a house, a bike , a mountain range,
a flower, a book, a toothbrush or a drum.

The way we walk, the way we jump and run
turns us into trains or scarecrows,
giraffes or octopuses, bouncing balls
or birds. The way we eat and sit and breathe

allows us to alter — we can be quite old,
like ancient warriors, or goddesses of Greece,
simply by taking thought; or transform ourselves
into the youngest things in all creation —

raindrops, grass, a new-discovered world, wild
strawberries, a baby elephant, a flame, a faun,
the first star of evening, a cloud shadow,
mysterious ripple on a lake, or a breeze of dawn —

All these, and countless other things we can become
at will, and through imagination re-create ourselves
into something familiar or funny, rich and strange —
for we are the children, the children of change.

DREAM

What is this ocean liner doing —
lights burning from stem to stern
and crimson smokestack smoking —
lying on its side in the middle of the Sahara?

Can it be a mirage reflected
from the bottom of the Atlantic?
If so, why are the propellers
working, churning, screwing up the sand
into tornadoes of dust and ash?
Why are the rusted anchors half-sunk in
the dunes' imperceptibly-shifting waves?

A drowned sailor,
head pillowed on his lifted collar,
sleeps in a hammock of sand.
The Sphinx looks shocked.
And all the Pyramids
are reclining on their elbows
like rows of faceless spectators
at this shipwreck's deserted oasis.

And why is that ancient lighthouse,
that should be in Alexandria,
standing here on a cloud that is a rock,
winking in time to the seagulls' cries?

SCARECROWS

Where I live, there are more
scarecrows than human beings.
They would not lift their hats
even if the Queen passed by.

A scarecrow is born old
and stupid. The birds
steal the seeds at his foot.
They know he can't kick back.

The autumn sparrows flit
from one scarecrow to the next.
Their rags and bones are
covered with falling leaves.

And once the harvest's in,
the scarecrow's no more use.
Winter comes, and the crows
perch on his battered straw hat.

Never ask a scarecrow
if he's feeling cold.
The pitiless wind and rain
have numbed him to the bone.

He seems to sleep standing.
The farmer goes to check
if he's still awake, and
kicks him just to make sure.

In the icy moonlight he looks
like some poor lost child.
And when it's raining
he almost seems human.

He turns his back on
the rays of the setting sun.
But his twisted shadow stretches
right across the lane.

Even a silly scarecrow
still has a nose and a mouth
and his big round eyes — more
frightening than any human's.

The old country folk here
are all bent and thin:
ashamed to be seen standing
next to their scarecrow ghosts.

SCARECROW INDEPENDENCE

(Variations on a haiku theme by Dansui)

I may look raggy and queer
— but I bow to no man.

My face may look silly and sad
—but I'm no snowman.

I may stand stiff and still
— but I hold my head up high.

I raise my old top hat to no one
— not even when *you* walk by.

Dansui was a 17th century Japanese haiku poet and his original
poem was something like this: "I raise my cap to no one — not even
the Emperor."

SCARECROW GHOST

In the twilight
under the trees'
green wind,
a ragged ghost
hopping on one
leg with arms
as stiff as
windmills but
unmoving — big
head a turnip
lantern unlit
the grin of an
idiot dog, so
skinny, thin as
a rake — it *is*
a rake, mouth
full of rusted
broken teeth,
gaps grinning
clods of clay
still sticking
been eating
earth and stones
this phantom
of rags and bones
one glove lost
the other found
fingers flapping
on the ground
beckoning to us
without a sound
in the twilight
under the trees'
green wind.

JAPANESE SCARECROW

An ancient cotton robe
flaps on my back.
My body is formed from
an old rice sack.

On my head
a conical hat.
In one hand a pink
plastic baseball bat.

My fingers are cheap
chopsticks, rattling cans
of one-yen coins. My feet,
broken paper fans.

My face is a battered
painted kite,
its pigtail dangling
out of sight.

My hair is sun-bleached
horse-tail frond,
so it may look
alarmingly blond.

Why have they given
my mad face these two
enormous eyes —
so round, so blue?

Because these are not
the eyes of Japan —
they are the eyes
of a foreigner man.

And therefore they frighten
the birds from the skies —
so round, so blue,
these enormous eyes!

ELECTRONIC SCARECROW

I'm programmed to frighten:
my traditional garb
old rags ricketty sticks
conceals a heart of wire,
a printout of behaviour.

My very soul
is a minimal computer
whose calculating spirit
sends out waves of noise.
My whole life is one small
generator of modulated
ultrasounds, using two
multivibrators with
a nominal frequency
regulated by my high
cutout frequency —
if I make myself clear.

Utilizing classic
BF amplifiers, current
tweeters as transconductors
I emit my ultrasounds —
perfectly inaudible
and inoffensive for
my master, man,
the village idiot, but
devastating for the birds,
those other
village idiots who don't know
what BF means.

Only when birds come near
am I triggered into action,
churning windmill arms,
shaking and shuddering,
twitching in grotesque display,
broadcasting hoots and howls,
recordings of buzzards,

vultures, hawks —
flashing electric eyes of owls.

But when the farmer
enters my field
he switches me off:
nothing scares him,
the idiot, though
occasionally
I manage to give him
an electric shock —
just a reminder that science is king.

THE FALLEN SCARECROW

He lies in the mud there, flat on his back,
with his old tweed cap knocked off.
A raggy straw rope round his elegant waist —
he must have once been quite a toff.

He still grins up at the rainy clouds
with his big round painted eyes.
His rotten rope fingers cannot zip up
his dungarees' unzipped flies.

How did he fall? Was he mugged by a gang?
— He's wearing still on his one lame foot
torn out of the clay like a twisted root
a long-dead labourer's army boot.

Should we try to set him up again?
Perhaps it's better to leave him there
grinning as if at some secret joke,
flat on his back, without a care.

— So lie in the mud there, flat on your back,
with your old tweed cap knocked off.
A raggy straw rope round your elegant waist —
you must once have been quite a toff.

SCARECROW DESPAIR

I'm supposed to be an awful fright
and scare the birds the livelong day.
But though I am a ghastly sight
I fail to frighten birds away.

I really look a dreadful mess
in filthy clothes and hat as well.
My head's a raving wilderness,
I really stink, not simply smell
to highest heaven, deepest hell.

O, what a proper scream I look —
a dropout in my soggy pants!
No matter what great pains I took
I couldn't even scare a rook.
Wind tears these ragged gloves my hands,
rain turns my heart to sinking sands.

My shadow looks just like a man's,
but I have neither love nor friends.
I wait here till my torture ends —
I have no future, make no plans.
Only myself I scare. The birds know I
could never even hurt a fly
and rain their droppings from the sky.

I'm supposed to be an awful fright,
and scare the birds the livelong day.
But though I am a ghastly sight
I fail to frighten birds away.

MY SLEDGE

As I drag it
over crusty snow
it follows me —
a dog at heel —
sometimes catching
up with me, now
at left, now at right,
sniffing my snowboots
with a soft bang
of its metal noses,
tip-tilted runners
shining-wet
that slither-slide
from side to side -

till they jerk back
at a bare patch, where
old snow has melted,
and there, like ponies
scenting bad water
or unseen dangers,
dig in their heels
and obstinately refuse
to move on to
the next good patch of snow,
where I can toboggan
from this hilltop height
into the soft snowdrifts
of meadows far below.

So I carry them over, and then
we are back in our element again.

UNICORN

I met a unicorn today —
four silver hooves all gleaming bright.
His coat was of a pearly grey,
his mane and tail of purest white.

His eyes were dark and warm and round
with eyelashes of fine pale silk.
He gently pawed the frosty ground
and snorted plumes like spectral milk.

And from the centre of his brow
one twisted horn of purest glass
sparkled beneath a snowy bough.
— I watched him slowly turn, and pass

into the sombre forest glade,
where he looked back at me, as though
to tell me not to be afraid,
and trust the crystal horn's soft glow.

I followed him, and very soon
he paused, till I reached his side.
Then, with the rising of the moon,
we set off on a wild night ride.

All night I lay along his back,
grasping that horn of purest glass.
We galloped down each forest track
till dawn sparked diamonds from the grass.

Then O! the frost all melted, and the snow:
the leaves all flashed with crystal dew!
But he had vanished — where I do not know...
Could this have been a dream? Or was it true?

TEACHERS

They're all right, in our school.
Some of them.
Not like in some schools I've been to.

Some are silly and soft,
some too severe and strict.
Only one or two
can be both funny and firm.

Some talk at you
as if you were hardly human —
as object, a name, a number.
They've got examinations on the brain.

But there's some, you can tell
they like you — they don't suck up,
say what you write is good
when you know it's bad,
or praise your painting
when it stinks.
They tell you straight.
Then you do it better for them.

Our sports instructor is a real pro.
He can you teach you anything, because
he can do it all himself —
how to bat and pitch better,
how to box and swim and score a try.
He takes us running round
the moat of the Imperial Palace,
and makes us do push-ups till we drop.

I only wish I could find
a teacher who could teach us maths.
The one we have just now
seems to live apart, in a world of his own,
and his speech is pure abstraction,
barely comprehensible. He talks to himself.

When he writes equations on the board
he seems to be floating in fractions,
in clouds of chalk and algebra.
I can't follow him. He doesn't want me to.

In geography, we colour maps
showing rainfall, population, physical
features the master cannot explain
to my satisfaction. We have to take him on trust
about the world beyond these islands.
— While we worry about Japan, so small,
like a performing seal balancing
Hokkaido on the nose of Honshu
seen through the wrong end of a telescope
far, far away on the very edge of the world.

History is dates and eras. In history lessons,
the centuries flash by in storms of falling cherry petals
and the teacher battles with the past
of treaties that are always broken:
he's always on the losing side.
History for us begins with Hiroshima, Nagasaki.
We visit them on school excursions,
and the teachers, trying to explain, quite fail
to understand why we cannot believe it's true:
perhaps because we don't want to. It could happen to us
again, they tell us. What can we do about it?
We feel an anger the teacher cannot show, and wonder:
why are we all so helpless?

I think I'd like to be a teacher.
It's sometimes terrible, being taught.
No wonder some of them get attacked.
We're often bored out of our skulls
by teachers.

But they're all right, in our school.
Some of them.

Translated by James Kirkup from the Japanese of a 15-year-old
schoolboy, Katayama Osamu.

EXTRA-CURRICULAR ACTIVITY

Writing a Poem to be Buried in a Time Capsule

Well, now, I hardly know just how I should begin.
In the first place, whom, exactly,
am I supposed to be addressing? Should I call you
Mr., Mrs., Miss or Ms? B.A.? M.A.? Or even Professor, Ph.D?
Or are you perhaps a "Sir" this or a "Lady" that?
(Highly unlikely, now I come to think of it —
the aristocracy already seems a dying race.)

Can you read English? I hope so. Can you even read?
They way things are going these days, poetry and books
may soon be things of the past. (What? No more comics?)
— Are you more or less like me? Or barely human? Invader
from outermost space, come at last to colonize our earth (if
there's anything left of it) with robot armies of right-wing kids?
(Today's lot are pretty spaced-out, on totalitarian trips.)

O.K. then, this is it. Whoever you are, this is my poem
that our English teacher, Sneakers, gave us to write for homework
on this far-out time capsule idea. At least forty lines!
(Personally, I think it's pretty weird. Whatever next?)
Then our class are going to take their poems, signed and dated,
after school next Monday, after they've been marked, corrected and
re-written in our best handwriting, to bury them on the Downs

in this really neat time-capsule they've made in Metalwork.
But what a crazy notion! I ask you, whoever you are,
who cares? What does it matter? And what's in it for me?
I can tell you the poems are sure to be a load of rubbish
like this one ...
                    — Or is it? I've only just realized I'm writing it
as if I fully expected it to be read in a hundred years' time
by you, mate, wherever, whoever or whatever you are. Good grief!

POEM TO BE BURIED IN A TIME CAPSULE

My poem is in itself
a kind of time capsule.
It contains my essence,
my native speech,
my choice of words,
my thought, my laughter
and my very breath.

You can swallow it
like a vitamin pill —
one that you absorb
through eyes and ears,
until your own lungs,
throat, tongue and lips
reconstitute its voice.

Through its lines you hear
my own voice speaking
across the centuries.
Though I have long been dead,
this poem is a living thing
from secret sources
that are still living.

Be careful as you
unearth my mystery, and
unwind my age-old wrappings
tenderly, with understanding
of my fragility, that hides
an unsuspected toughness
preserving precious seeds.

— Because a time capsule poem
is also a kind of time bomb
whose delayed-action meanings
can only be safely defused
by those who learn to read
between the lines. — Otherwise
I self-destruct! So mind what you do.

SCHOOL SPORTS DAY

The flags are streaming in a sunny breeze —
blue, green, yellow, red and white
above the freshly-whitewashed running tracks
all round the grassy sports-ground. New-mown,
the field's lush edges still are starred
with buttercups and daisies, dandelion clocks.

Music plays. From time to time the starter's pistol
explodes whole colonies of rooks from leafy elms
under whose shade old boys and parents and the Head
cheer on the last relay teams, the first heats of the sprints,
while (Ooh!) the pole-vaulter does a spacewalk from his pole,
the high-jumper bounces after her beautiful Fosbury flop.

Tea-urns hiss in the warm marquee. Coke bottles sweat.
Bright bunting drapes the plastic tablecloths
on which the paper plates of sandwiches and pies,
hot sausage-rolls and sugar buns and home-made cakes
attract the orchard wasps — and hungry boys and girls
flushed with the final heats, the prize-giving's proud applause.

As the long day cools to evening, we wander, tired
and stiff, but glad it's over, down the country lanes,
accompanying relatives and friends to sylvan car-parks
or the village station and its cottage flower-beds.
— Then slowly back to school for evening prayers,
lights out, larks, laughter — and dreams of coming holidays.

FIRST ART LESSON

My new paintbox's shining black lacquer lid
divided neatly into three oblong sections
reflects my funny face, the art room windows
white with autumn clouds and flecked with rain.

When I open it, the scented white enamel dazzles.
Inside, pure colours are displayed like blocks
of a bulb-grower's bed of flowers, toy spectrum
in china tubs and tin tubes, a cubist rainbow.

From my jamjar filled with fresh water at the sink
I pour a little liquid into each depression;
take the brush of silky camel hair; wet its plumpness
for the first time, and the last, between my lips.

Then dip its fine, dark tip into the water-tanks
and into juicy wells of Crimson Lake, Gamboge, Sienna,
Peacock Blue, Burnt Ochre, Emerald, Olive, Terracotta,
Vermilion, Umber, Cadmium, Indigo, Intense Black.

Damp the paper. From the top edge, with a sleek, loaded brush,
begin to release the first phantom of a pale-blue wash.

Me and my best friend
we like to go down to the station
and get our pictures taken
in one of those photo machines
you know, where you
put the money in, then
sit on the seat inside and
draw the little curtain
waiting for the four flashes.

Me and my best friend
we like to pull funny faces
and act silly, wearing
red noses and paper hats
with hello sailor printed on them
and get our pictures taken
together like that, two
for the price of one, like,

and sometimes what comes out
nearly kills us with laughing, or
frightens the living daylights out of
me and my best friend.

*   *   *

I was taking a picture of the harbour
when the heavy camera slipped a little
between my hands. Fortunately, I did not
drop it. But - smile, please, say "cheese" or
"stewed prunes" - the shutter had already clicked.

Among the snaps of friends and family groups
that was the most interesting shot of all —
a tilted horizon, a leaning lighthouse almost up-
side down in a dragonish cloud, and at the bottom
just the top of somebody's straw hat.

THE TREE VOYAGE

We clamber into the branches
of the leaning apple tree
as if we were climbing,
hand over hand,
the cordage of an ancient schooner.
How the rigging creaks
and rocks in the orchard winds!

At the top of the rolling tree
(don't be seasick!)
we brace bare feet against
the swaying mainmast of the pitching trunk.
Here, up high in a crow's nest of new twigs,
above the spread sails of sunlit blossom,
we scan the green horizons
for Barbary pirates, galleons, ocean liners,
for sharks, mermaids, dolphins, spouting whales.

Or for the lonely albatross
that comes with its giant wings
and perches harmlessly beside us,
come to be friends with us
from far over the oceans of rustling leaves
from far over latitudes
and longitudes of rustling waves,
where birds fly like fish,
fish swim like birds.

We have a happy ship, so
we do not crucify our albatross.

CARNATION, LILY, LILY, ROSE

(John Singer Sargent)

Deep in the twilit garden, in the long grass,
among darkening leaves, bamboos and bushes
the summer flowers are still in bloom —
clove-scented carnations, pale lilies,
pink old-fashioned pom-pom roses.

Two little girls in white smocked dresses
frilled innocently at neck and hem
wear sensible black stockings, plain strapped shoes.
They are preparing for a party, lighting
neatly-slung strings of Japanese lanterns.

Their rounded cheeks softly glow, as they
bend their heads over lacquered mouths of paper globes
and flowered concertinas that they are carefully lighting
with wooden tapers, or with long kitchen matches,
while all around them lighted lanterns shine

like rising moons among the fading flowers,
and hang the leaves with firelit paper petals.

(Tate Gallery, London)

A LETTER TO FATHER CHRISTMAS

Dear Sir, you must think it very strange
that I haven't written for so long -
five or six years, in fact - I who
so often pestered you with my lists.

But the truth is, they told me long ago
you didn't exist, and I must admit
I felt quite sad, even though I learned
to laugh at you, and at my foolish wishes.

"There is no Santa Claus!" I remember how I ran
through the snowy streets that winter day,
shouting my discovery, tears in my eyes, but
pretending to be in the know at last, grown-up.

You must have heard us making fun of you
c/o the North Pole where I used to send my lists.
I hope you didn't feel too hurt,
or think we were awfully impolite.

But even as I laughed at you, I wept, and thought
I had lost a friend, an unseen, generous uncle,
a kind grandpa with a long white beard,
wearing a long red dressing-gown, carrying a sack.

And ever since that day, I have wished
that you were true. — So this is why
I'm writing, just to tell you, Sir,
you are the magic, the fantastic in my daily life —

like UFO's, Loch Ness Monsters, Big Feet, the chance
of life on other planets, trips in outer space:
of one day meeting some fantabulous pop star
or winning the Pools — that's what you mean to me.

And that's why secretly I like you still,
and I believe in you, in spite of all they say
until the very end of all my days.
(You won't let them know I told you so.)

So here's wishing you a Merry Christmas and
a Happy New Year — and many of them, Sir.
Yours faithfully (and I mean it) — the boy who
used to call up the chimney, now going on thirteen.

SNOWY DAY AT SCHOOL

Five Haiku

Overnight, the snow
has turned into one long slope
our five schoolyard steps.

No one can sit on
the playground swings, buried deep
under drifts of snow.

In still-falling snow
perching crows shake trees of flakes
in still-falling snow.

Classroom radiant
with snowlight. Your face reflects
each slow-turning page.

The whole classroom seems
to start silently rising
in still-falling snow.

THE DESERTED PLAYGROUND

No one is playing
in the freezing rain.

Not even a stray dog
runs among the puddles.

The swings are still.
Their worn seats are all wet.

The jungle gym
is covered with pigeon droppings,
slippery and dangerous —
whoever climbs in it
will fall from bar to bar
like a lost ball
bouncing through the bare
branches of a winter tree.

The slide's flight of iron steps
is rusty, and still standing.
But the slide itself
is no longer there.

— That is why
ghosts of dead children
keep climbing the steps
in the freezing rain
and jumping off
            into space
with silent
screams of terror.

A RITE OF SUMMER

Here at the Nagaoka Tenjin Junior High School
some of the girls are washing schoolroom windows,
boys are weeding and sweeping the vast, dusty playground.

But the children there down below my apartment
are busy cleaning out the swimming-pool.
I watch them from my balcony, five storeys up.

After the long winter, the evil-looking, dark green water
with its sinister sediments and vegetable stinks
has finally been let out, leaving a glorious mess behind.

Some of that rich dirt was plum or apricot blossoms
and snowstorms of windblown cherry petals,
or autumn's maples, crimson-leafed, and ginkgo gold.

But now the barefoot schoolchildren, a whole class of thirty-five,
are scrubbing clean the skyblue tiles, the black guidelines
with brooms and hoses, kitchen scrubbers and plastic pails.

Much of the tapwater is playfully splashed on brown-limbed boys
and laughing girls in blue trunks and white T-shirts
till they are soaked to the skin — a kind of annual rite

before the long summer races down those six deep lanes,
now dry, that soon will fill with divers' cries
of joy, and glittering reflections of a cloudless sky.

Nagaoka Tenjin Haitsu   *May 19th, 1984*

THE SIX SENSES

Touch

At the end of each finger
there is a kind of feeling eye
that even in the dark can tell us
what is cold, hot, wet or dry.

The palms can show us
what is smooth or rough.
Our teeth inform us
what is soft or tough.

Our whole body is a vast computer
of small antennae, an electric hutch
of sensors weaving the cloth of life
with touch after touch, touch after touch.

Hearing

Put the sea-shell to your ear,
and what do you hear?
You hear the ocean waves, the red
tides within your head.

But with the other ear, you still
hear the world outside, the shrill
cries the seagulls make, a baby's screech,
and real waves pounding on a real beach.

Sight

Close your eyes, and press
your fingers gently on the lids —
a kind of personal kaleidoscope
of colours, shapes and faces
keeps changing and shifting,
dreaming and drifting.

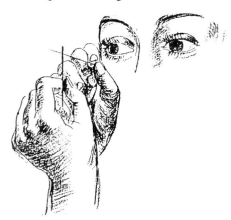

That is one kind of sight —
the things we see in sleep
or in imagination's mirror.
— But true sight is better:
so open your eyes at last, and see
the real world of you and me.

Taste

Sweet or sour, sharp or bitter —
what is the taste on your tongue?
A spoonful of porridge, a mouthful of jam —
even with eyes closed tight
we know what they are,
for lips, tongue and palate
tell what is good or bad,
what is nasty or nice —
like cod-liver oil
or a chocolate ice.

Smell

Some people are all nose —
and I don't mean nosy.
They are most sensitive to smells
of every kind, the nicest and nastiest,
the strongest, sweetest, faintest.

Dogs, cats and all living creatures
live by smell: their lives depend
upon a knowing nostril
for the scent of danger in the wind,
or the call of food, or weather's change.

It would be terrible to have no nose: we well know
what it's like when we catch the 'flu
and can't smell anything at all
(or taste anything, too). The nose is a nuisance
when all it can do is sniff, snuffle and sneeze.

For smell is perhaps the most delicate
of all the senses, and that is why
we have so many words for it, and they all
mean something different — just think! —
scent, perfume, aroma, odour, stench and stink!

Sixth Sense

What is it? What
makes us suddenly look round
as if we suddenly expected to be found
out doing what we should not?
Or sensing we might be shot
or stabbed or thrown to the ground
by something unseen
coming just behind us? What
on earth can it be?
       Or in the green
depths of a quiet wood, what
makes us carefully pause, then shiver
and shake and quiver? What is it? What
makes us inexplicably feel both cold and hot,
and sets our hair on end? O, What
message does it send,
what secret we forgot?
And why do we know
this sixth sense so?

HIGH STREET SMELLS

A busy street is a public library of smells —
the coffee grinder's fresh aroma at the corner,
the baker's sweet, buttery perfume —
you can almost taste the rolls, the pastries,
and drink the toasted coffee on the morning air.

Out of the sweet shops and the candy stores
oozes the exotic scent of marzipan and chocolate,
and the plebeian breath of chewing gum and gobstoppers.
The fruit market is a pungent orchard of essential juices,
and my ever-wary nose tells me that I'm approaching
the butcher's, with its plain whiffs of blood and sawdust,
while the sea itself comes swimming right across the pavement
as I pass the fishmonger's briny bouquets in ice and salt.

The Chinese takeaway, the Indian curry restaurant,
the fish-and-chip shop, McDonald's (smell is flavour),
the Olde Worlde Teashoppe, all have their distinctive auras
and tangs of sweet and sour, poppadoms and spice,
deep-frying oil with vinegar. And toast, cakes and tea.

A gush of ironing steam from the laundry. The dry cleaner's
sharp, stinging reek, like smelling-salts — what a pong!
The pubs are open books of beer, wines and spirits
that my nostrils read rapidly, a kind of boozy braille.
The shoe emporium's rich emanations of supple leather, new shoes
impregnating the shoe boxes' pure white cardboard and tissue paper.
And here's the newsagent's — you can almost read the acrid print
of the local weekly, "The Farming World," "The People's Friend,"
"Popular Gardening" — and all the comics before you even open them!
The voluptuous tobacconist's censes with its musky leaf
an entire shopping-mall — the drums, cartons and boxes
of honeyed shag, and tins of teasing snuff.

These are just some of the olfactory treats
for the aware nostril, the adventurous nose
seeking, among the banal stink and stench of exhaust fumes
the characters, the eccentrics, the silent friends
that are the original fragrances of busy streets.

CONVERSATIONS

Talking to Myself

I like talking to myself when I'm alone -
usually silently, but sometimes out loud
as when I'm constructing a complicated model
or practising new chords on my guitar:
or when I hit my thumb with a hammer,
or prick my finger - but what I say then
can hardly be called polite conversation.

Some people say it's the first sign of madness,
but I don't think so. Perhaps for company, we all
talk to ourselves in some way or other,
making remarks about what the weather's like or what's the time.

Of course, I mostly talk to myself in English:
but try talking to yourself in some foreign language
or one you've made up yourself, like the one
I use when chatting to my dog or my budgie —
the words are English, but they hardly make sense
except to them and me. And that's what conversation is:
communication with yourself, between yourself and others.
But often the best conversations are speech without words,
exchanging thoughts — with yourself or others
                                        — in speaking silences.

Overheard in the High Street

I've never seen anything like it Edna —
That's right Maud I agree with you —
It's really terrible the way they do go on —
They're really awful, dear, it's true.

You can hardly walk the streets these days —
That's just what I was saying to Mr. Winterbottom — so queer
And the clothes they wear, and those funny boots and bags —
I know, I know — they call them "gear."

I wouldn't let my lot be seen with them —
It doesn't look respectable you know —
And on the buses, the way they all behave —
They don't seem to have a proper place to go —

And honestly, the language and the make-up —
and their spiky hair, all colours, really shockers —
Who are they, anyhow, who do they think they are? —
Maud, they call them punks, and mods and rockers.

CHANGES

That's the house where we used to live —
we left it less than a year ago.
It's the first time I've seen it again —
how could it have altered so?

For one thing, the name on the gate
is new. They now call it "Andermatt."
(It used to be "Palma" when we were there).
— How could they change our name for that?

The curtains are different, too, of course —
ours were pale lemon yellow and white:
but theirs are a horrible purple and pink —
as our mother remarked: "Oh my! What a sight!"

At the back window that was once my room
a strange kind of doll is on guard:
my robot monster used to stand there
laser-beaming the next backyard.

There's a new car inside the garage —
a trim Toyota. (Ours was a Ford).
And out in the garden, by the front door,
two bicycles lean, and a windsail board.

— But some things they could never change:
the warm red bricks, the laburnam in bloom,
the shape of the path, the steps at the back,
the bow windows of the living room.

Yet as we drive past, the familiar street
no longer seems long, or the trees so high —
O, what has become of the places I knew?
Has our old house really changed? Or have I?

PRINCE GENJI : THE CHRYSANTHEMUM DOLL

Lifesize, on a frame of bamboo and straw
approximating human form, and fragrant,
the doll stands in its theatre of green,
and smiles on all the passers-by.

Like some male floral deity, he wears
jerkin and cloak of mauve chrysanthemums —
small, neat, closely-set, like an embroidery.
His arms ripple with sleeves of pale pink asters.

His pantaloons are Michaelmas daisies,
and his petalled hair blows in the breeze.
His armour of bronze bachelor button varieties,
his gauntlets of mingled white and yellow buds.

Refreshed by occasional showers, or
by the fine mists gently sprayed upon him from
the cupid cheeks and lips of the old doll master,
he is still there at dawn, glittering with dew.

His wide eyes are deep blue cosmos,
his cheeks and mouth of everlastings,
his helmet quilled with golden petals. But
that bared sword is the real thing.

— Slowly, he loses his first scented brilliance,
gradually withers, sadly fades and shrinks.
At night, awaiting cremation in his flowered grave-clothes,
he lies half-rotten on the rubbish heap. Still smiling.

ZEN LEGEND

"Master, how may I find
the secret of life?"
— "Go into the remotest wilderness,
and when you have found it,
come and tell me."

The disciple went into
the remotest wilderness.
For one year
he meditated.
But when he came to tell the Master
what he had found, the Master said:
"No, you have not found it."

So the disciple went back into
the remotest wilderness.
For five years
he meditated.
But when he came to tell the Master
what he had found, the Master said:
"No, you have not found it."

So the disciple went back again into
the remotest wilderness,
and without seeking for it
immediately found it.

But when he had found it
he did not come to tell the Master.

Then the Master
knew he had found it.

FOR OLD TIMES' SAKE

(a tree speaks)

I live out my life
in these widening rings
like a thrown stone's ripples
from the centre of things.

I grew with each year
in sunshine and dark:
each ripple expanded
my long coat of bark.

How small my beginnings,
the seed of my heart —
but growing and flowing
with life from the start.

So many bird songs
are caught in my grooves,
and voices, and laughter,
and wild horses' hooves!

I once hid a king
and a highwayman bold:
I've seen thousands of seasons
but don't feel that old.

In winter I'm leafless,
my heart's in my roots.
But when spring comes, the sun
drives new life through my shoots.

I've been struck by the lightning,
been battered by gales:
but through rain, snow and tempest
my faith never fails.

It may be this ring
is the last I shall make,
but I keep the rings turning —
for old times' sake.

Goslar, March 1980

FOR THE PLANTING OF A TREE:

MEMORY FROM BEYOND THE TOMB
(after Chateaubriand)

The tree I planted is still a child,
with a child's stature, a child's grace.
— But no children ever grew so wild,
or offered the sun more trustful face.

When I stand beside this little one,
my shadow protects and shields its frailty.
— Even so, when I am old, may sun
be tempered for me by this little tree.

And my present gift of shade be given back
a thousand times, a thousand times,
till all is shadow,
and all suns are black.

COMPARISONS

I was thinking it was a dead leaf
blowing slowly along the path —
then I saw it was a fieldmouse.

I was thinking the village pond
had red flowers growing out of it —
then I saw they were Coca Cola cans.

I was thinking it was a green frog
panting by the side of the slimy pool —
then I saw it was a wind-stirred bubble gum wrapper.

I was thinking it was a seagull
flying and hanging on the autumn wind —
then I saw it was only a bit of greasy chip paper.

I was thinking it was a melting snowflake
on the dark windowpane last night —
then I saw it was the waning moon.

I was thinking it was a girl waving to me
from an upper room, with a yellow handkerchief —
then I saw she was just washing the window.

— I was thinking reality was better
than illusion, than what I'd thought I'd seen.
But then I saw they were equal, and part of each other.